Exam Success

Inspection and Testing 2391-10

Jonathan Elliott and Mark Coles

First published 2008
© 2008 The City and Guilds of London Institute.
All answers to examination questions © 2008
The Institution of Engineering and Technology.

City & Guilds is a trademark of the City and
Guilds of London Institute.
The IEE is an imprint of the Institution of
Engineering and Technology.

ISBN: 978-0-86341-899-0

Every effort has been made to ensure that the
information contained in this publication is
true and correct at the time of going to press.
However, examination products and services
are subject to continuous development and
improvement and the right is reserved to
change products and services from time
to time. While the authors, publishers and
contributors believe that the information
and guidance given in this work is correct,
all parties must rely upon their own skill and
judgement when making use of it. Neither the
authors, the publishers nor any contributor
assume any liability to anyone for any loss or
damage caused by any error or omission in
the work, whether such error or omission is
the result of negligence or any other cause.
Where reference is made to legislation it is not
to be considered as legal advice. Any and all
such liability is disclaimed.

Cover and book design by CDT Design Ltd
Implementation by Adam Hooper, Hoop Design
Typeset in Congress Sans and Gotham
Printed in the UK by Burlington Press

Exam Success

Inspection and Testing 2391-10

Jonathan Elliott and Mark Coles

City & Guilds Level 3 Certificate in Inspection, Testing and Certification of Electrical Installations (2391-10)

City & Guilds is the UK's leading provider of vocational qualifications, offering over 500 awards across a wide range of industries, and progressing from entry level to the highest levels of professional achievement. With over 8500 centres in 100 countries, City & Guilds is recognised by employers worldwide for providing qualifications that offer proof of the skills they need to get the job done.

Copies may be obtained from:
Teaching & Learning Materials
City & Guilds
1 Giltspur Street
London EC1A 9DD
For publications enquiries:
T +44 (0)20 7294 4113
F +44 (0)20 7294 3414
E-mail learningmaterials@cityandguilds.com

The Institution of Engineering and Technology is the new institution formed by the joining together of the IEE (The Institution of Electrical Engineers) and the IIE (The Institution of Incorporated Engineers). The new institution is the inheritor of the IEE brand and all its products and services including the IEE Wiring Regulations (BS 7671), the IEE Code of Practice and supporting material.

Copies may be obtained from:
The Institution of Engineering and Technology
PO Box 96
Stevenage
SG1 2SD, UK
T +44 (0)1438 767 328
E-mail sales@theiet.org
www.theiet.org

Contents

Introduction

How to use this book

This book is designed to be a study aid for the written examination assessment (2391-301) of the City & Guilds Level 3 Certificate in Inspection, Testing and Certification of Electrical Installations (2391-10). It sets out methods of studying, offers advice on preparation for the written exam and provides details of the scope and structure of this examination, alongside two full sample tests with sample answers and detailed guidance from examiners. Used as a study guide for exam preparation and practice, it will help you to reinforce and test your existing knowledge, and will give you guidelines and advice about sitting the exam. You should try to answer the sample test papers under exam conditions (or as close as you can get) and then review all of your answers. This will help you to become familiar with the types of question that might be asked in the exam and will also give you an idea of how to pace yourself in order to complete all the questions comfortably within the time limit. This book cannot guarantee a positive exam result, but it can play an important role in your overall revision programme, enabling you to focus your preparation and approach the exam with confidence.

City & Guilds Level 3 Certificate in Inspection, Testing and Certification of Electrical Installations (2391-10)

This qualification is intended for experienced people working in the electrical industry. Although City & Guilds does not state formal candidate entry requirements, the qualification is not intended for non-qualified electricians and/or those who do not have experience in inspecting, testing and certifying electrical installations. Candidates without this experience should consider undertaking the Level 2 Certificate in Fundamental Inspection, Testing and Initial Verification (2392-10) as well as obtaining industry experience. It is also strongly recommended that candidates should have achieved either the City & Guilds Certificate in the Requirements for Electrical Installations (BS 7671: 2008) (2382-10) or a similar qualification demonstrating knowledge and understanding of the 17th Edition of the *IEE Wiring Regulations* (BS 7671).

The aim of this qualification is to enable the candidate to develop the necessary technical knowledge and understanding about the inspection, testing and certification of electrical installations. The certificate is assessed by one written examination, for which this book is intended to provide help, and also by one practical assessment.

Finding a centre

In order to take the exam, you must register at an approved City & Guilds centre. You can find your nearest centre by looking up the qualification number 2391-10 on www.cityandguilds.com. The IET (Institution of Engineering and Technology) is an accredited centre and runs exams in different parts of the country. For more details, see www.theiet.org.

At each centre, the Local Examinations Secretary will enter you for the award, collect your fees, arrange for your assessments to take place and correspond with City & Guilds on your behalf. The Local Examinations Secretary also receives your certificates and any correspondence from City & Guilds. Most centres will require you to attend a course of learning before entering you for the assessments. These are usually available as day or evening courses, over a number of weeks. Your local centre will advise you of their particular course availability.

Awarding of certificates

When you undertake the City & Guilds 2391-10 assessments, a certificate will be issued only when you have been successful in both the written and practical assessments. This certificate will not indicate a grade or percentage pass. Your centre will receive your Notification of Candidate's Results for the written assessment and then the certificate once both assessment components are successfully completed.

Any correspondence is conducted through your centre. The centre will also receive a consolidated results list detailing the performance of all candidates entered for the written assessment at their centre. City & Guilds also provides notification of successful completion of the practical assessment to the centre. This is following the centre's submission of all candidates' successful completion of the practical assessments to City & Guilds.

If you have particular requirements that will affect your ability to attend and take the examinations, then your centre should refer to City & Guilds policy document 'Access to Assessment: Candidates with Particular Requirements'.

Notes

The exam

The exam

The exam in brief

The aim of this qualification is to enable the candidate to develop the necessary technical knowledge and understanding about the inspection, testing and certification of electrical installations.

For this qualification, candidates are required to complete the following assessments:
- **one** written assessment
- **one** practical assessment.

Unit 301 – Written examination

The exam paper contains 26 questions and is 2.5 hours long. It is divided into two sections. Section A consists of 20 short-answer questions worth 60 marks (approximately 1 hour). Section B consists of 6 structured questions worth 90 marks (approximately 1.5 hours).

	Topic/outcome	No of questions	Marks	%
Section A	Preparation for inspection and testing	3	9	6
	Inspection	2	6	4
	Testing	15	45	30
Section B	Preparation for inspection and testing			
	Inspection	6	90	60
	Testing			
	Totals	26	150	100

Unit 302 – Practical assessment

The practical assessment element must also be completed to obtain the 2391-10 certificate. Full details can be obtained from your centre.

Guidance on sitting the written examination

Notes

This section provides some useful information about the 2391-10 written examination (Unit 301) that you may find helpful. It considers:

- the format of the exam
- the structure of the exam
- how to interpret the questions and understand what is expected
- effective methods of answering questions.

It also identifies areas of the exam that are often not answered well and some of the most common errors that candidates make.

Format of the exam

The format of the examination is a written paper, which is divided into two sections, A and B, with 26 questions in total. The total number of marks available for the paper is 150. You are allowed two and a half hours to sit the exam and are expected to answer all the questions. It is a 'closed book' examination, which means that you are **not** allowed to take any notes or reference books into the exam with you.

Stucture of the exam

Section A is the short-answer section of the paper, which contains 20 questions with each question being worth three marks. Each question may be divided into three parts (a, b and c), with each part being worth one mark. Certain questions may only have two parts, with one worth two marks and the other a single mark.

Section A is made up of questions from three key subject areas:

- preparation for inspection and testing (3 questions)
- the process of inspection (2 questions)
- testing (15 questions).

There is a total of 60 marks available for these first 20 questions.

Section B is made up of six structured, long-answer questions. These questions are based upon an electrical installation scenario. They cover the range of subjects listed for Section A but examine the level of knowledge and understanding in more depth. There are 90 marks available for this section of the paper.

Interpreting questions and understanding what is expected

There are a couple of points that need to be considered when reading the questions:

Consider the number of marks available for the question

This provides a valuable indication of the depth of the answer required. For example, a question which carries one mark will require a much simpler answer than one for which 15 marks are available.

Read carefully and answer what the question actually asks

Often a question is answered incorrectly because of a failure to understand what is being asked and what is required. It is an easy trap to fall into under exam conditions where you are under pressure. The danger here is that you may answer a question to which you know the answer, but which is not the question you have been asked in the paper. Remember, the questions are set to establish your level of understanding in specific areas, so the correct response is important if the marks are to be obtained. Take a little longer to read the question carefully to ensure you are quite clear about what is required.

Wording of questions

The wording of a question, coupled with the number of marks available, gives valuable clues as to what is expected. The words used in the question provide the first clue. If you look out for the following words and phrases and understand what they mean, you should be able to provide an appropriate answer.

State: This means the answer is expected to be a short statement, not a long or rambling paragraph. The response to this type of question may even only be a single word or group of words – it does not need to be a complete sentence, so don't waste your valuable time writing one.

List: This means you should produce a simple list of items or actions. The answer should be similar to that produced for the 'state' question. However, on this occasion the items would be expected to follow a sequence and form a list, as would be expected for a shopping trip.

Explain briefly: This requires a brief explanation; usually no more than one or two sentences. It does not require paragraphs of explanation and the word 'briefly' is used to indicate this requirement.

Explain with the aid of a diagram: This means exactly what is says. The answer should comprise **both** a diagram and an explanation. Providing just the diagram or the explanation alone will not be sufficient to secure all the marks available for the question, as the total marks are divided between the diagram and the explanation.

Show all calculations: This phrase means that calculations are necessary for the marks to be obtained. You are required to show all your calculations so that you can demonstrate your understanding of the process used to calculate the answer. It allows the examiner to award marks for the correct process even if the figures used and the final answer are incorrect. Marks for these questions are divided up and allocated to both the method and the answer. A correct answer with no calculations will score only a small percentage of the overall marks available for the question.

With the aid of a fully labelled diagram: This indicates that a diagram needs to be provided with the component parts clearly labelled. The marks for these questions are divided between the diagram and the labelling. To obtain the maximum marks for the question both the labelling and the diagram must be completed.

Describe: Questions that ask you to 'describe' come up in Section B. They are often related to test procedures and you are required to demonstrate your knowledge of the test process. Look at the number of marks available to give you an indication of how much detail you need to go into.

Direct measurement: This indicates that a test is required and the results are **not** to be established by using a calculation. For example, where you are asked to describe the direct measurement of earth fault loop impedance, then a description of the test procedure is required. Describing an $R_1 + R_2$ test and then stating how to determine the value by calculation using $Z_s = Z_e + (R_1 + R_2)$ will result in no marks being awarded for the answer.

Terminology

It is important to answer questions using the correct terminology, which is the same as that used in Guidance Note 3 and BS 7671. Always use the correct titles and terminology. Brand names should **not** be used to describe items of equipment, test instruments and the like. For example, the instrument used to test for continuity is a low-resistance ohmmeter. It should not be referred to using a manufacturer's name (eg Megger) or referred to as a continuity tester, since the precise performance requirements of the

Notes

particular instruments are given in BS 7671 and Guidance Note 3 and some instruments and continuity testers that provide continuity features may not meet the requirements of BS 7671.

Multifunction test instruments are quite common in electrical installation testing. You need to be aware of the individual functions and ranges of these instruments. This includes such functions as insulation resistance and continuity and the appropriate measurement scales for each test. Also be careful to use the correct symbols to describe test instrument readings (mΩ, Ω, MΩ, A, kA, etc).

The use of the correct terminology for the component parts of an electrical system is also important. The application of the terms used in BS 7671 is necessary as this leaves no doubt as to the part being described. Typical items of equipment include the earthing conductor, main protective bonding conductors and circuit protective conductors. Terms such as 'earthwires' or 'cross bonding' do not correctly identify components and the examiner is then unable to award marks for these items.

Another common error is the use of incorrect titles for documents. If you refer to the 'Electricity at Work Act' instead of the 'Electricity at Work Regulations' or the 'Health and Safety at Work Regulations' instead of the 'Health and Safety at Work Act', this will result in no marks being awarded.

Common problem areas for Section B

In Section B of the paper the questions are all related to the scenario given at the start of the section. This scenario gives details of an electrical installation, or part of an installation. It identifies what work is to be carried out and provides information that is to be used to answer the questions in Section B. This means that the Section B answers should all relate to the installation identified in the scenario.

The most significant problem in this section is failing to read the scenario and apply the information given to the Section B questions. For example, when the scenario clearly states a TN-C-S system is used and a question asks for a diagram of the earth fault loop path, producing a drawing of a TN-S system will result in no marks being awarded for that question.

It may be beneficial for you to highlight key pieces of information in the scenario. This will help you to concentrate on what you are reading and will make referencing information easier when you are answering the questions.

You are expected to be able to describe the procedures for carrying out activities, including the inspection and testing of installations and circuits. These descriptions should follow the format given in Guidance Note 3.

Common errors in Section B answers are:
- no confirmation that testing can proceed
- no isolation procedure mentioned when it is appropriate
- no instrument and lead check carried out
- incorrect procedures described, such as not being able to describe the three steps in Guidance Note 3 for ring final circuit continuity
- not describing the test process in the correct sequence
- failure to consider the safety aspects necessary for the testing process
- failure to reinstate the installation safely once testing is complete.

Confirmation of compliance

Some questions are included to determine your ability to confirm that measured test results actually meet the requirements of BS 7671. In order to do this you will be expected to show what steps are taken for this process and any calculations that may be involved. You will also be expected to identify appropriate action for any situations where the results do not meet the requirements. This will extend to identifying appropriate remedial action to achieve compliance of the circuits or installation.

A common area for error is the application of the 'rule of thumb' to the maximum tabulated values of earth fault loop impedance (these are given in the scenario or question information) in order to compare these with the measured values. When candidates do not correctly apply the rule of thumb, it shows they are unable to correctly identify compliance with BS 7671 and therefore no marks are awarded.

Forms of certification and documentation

Section B questions may include the completion of any of the forms of certification identified in BS 7671 and Guidance Note 3. These forms are expected to be completed in relation to the installation described in the scenario.

Possible forms include:
- Electrical Installation **Certificate**
- Periodic Inspection **Report**
- **Schedule** of Inspections
- **Schedule** of Test Results
- Minor Electrical Installation Works **Certificate**.

Notes

Notes

The completion of forms requires you to identify the information provided in the scenario, and the subsequent questions, and use this to complete the forms correctly. You should ensure that you are familiar with the content of the forms of certification and other documents and that you understand how to complete them correctly. The questions that require completion of forms and documents are 'negatively marked'. This means that if, for example, 15 marks are available for the completion of a schedule of inspections, you start with 15 marks. A mark is then deducted for each item that is incorrectly completed. This also includes any relevant information omitted from the form or document. If you are not able to correctly fill in the forms and documents then the whole 15 marks can easily be lost.

Where forms and documents are given for you to complete, they are often printed double-sided. You should always check both sides of the form or document to ensure that you complete it entirely. Missing out the second page will result in no marks being awarded for the question, as all the second-page items will be missing from your answer.

Putting your answers on paper

There are many ways in which questions can be answered and you will need to find the method that best suits you. Here are some hints to help you decide on a style.

It is important to remember when you are answering the questions that the examiners cannot:
- ask further questions to establish your understanding – they can only award marks for the information you provide
- assume what you mean or know – they can only interpret the information they are given in your answers.

Due to the time constraints of the exam, do **not** waste time by copying out the question. The examiner already has a copy of the questions. As long as you correctly number each answer, there is no need to write the questions out.

The marking of the exam papers does not include any penalties or extra marks for spelling or grammar. However, the examiners will still need to be able to read your answers and handwriting, so write as clearly as possible. Providing the examiners can understand your response (and the answer is correct), then marks will be awarded.

The answers do not need to be in the form of an essay or long, descriptive text. A simple step-by-step approach to the answer provides you with an easy reference as to what you have included when you read back through the answer. It also allows you to insert any item you have missed and indicate the correct location to the examiner.

Short-answer questions (Section A)

For the 'state' and 'list' type of questions in Section A, the response should be quite simple.

Question: **State** three documents that specifically relate to electrical installations.

Answer:
- BS 7671
- Guidance Note 3
- The On-Site Guide

Question: **List** the first three tests to be carried out on a newly installed radial circuit.

Answer:
1) Continuity of protective conductors
2) Insulation resistance
3) Polarity

When asked to state items, bullet points can be used and no particular sequence is required. Where you are asked for the first three tests you should identify these in number sequence. Remember, if you are asked to list something in sequence then the items must be given in the correct order or you will lose marks.

For 'explain briefly' type questions, the answers should be short and to the point.

Question: **Explain briefly** what effect the increase in length has on conductor resistance.

Answer 1:   Conductor resistance increases as the length of the conductor increases.

Answer 2:   Conductor resistance is directly proportional to conductor length.

Both answers contain no unnecessary information but demonstrate that you are fully aware of the relationship between conductor length and conductor resistance, as asked.

Notes

Structuring long answers (Section B)

In Section B you will often be asked for longer answers, by questions that ask you to 'describe'. These are often related to test procedures and you are required to demonstrate your knowledge of the test process.

For example:
Describe the procedure for carrying out an insulation resistance test on a newly installed lighting circuit. (10 marks)

There are a number of pointers in this question. The answer is worth 10 marks so it will need to be more than a short, one-line answer. The question tells you the circuit is a new lighting circuit. From this you can determine that the insulation resistance test should be carried out before the circuit is to be energised for the first time. Therefore your answer will not need to include a description of the consultation process, or the isolation procedure.

Option 1

The answer could be provided as a description of the process in a 'story' format, as in the following.

I would prepare the cable for termination at the distribution board and carry out the insulation resistance test on the circuit before the final connection is made. I would first ensure that any voltage-sensitive or electronic equipment was linked out or removed to prevent damage during the test. I would select an insulation resistance test instrument and check that the instrument was in calibration and the leads were in a suitable condition. I would confirm that the instrument batteries were in good condition and the instrument was functioning by testing with the leads separated and then connected together. One lead of the instrument would then be connected to the line conductor and the other to the cpc. With the instrument set at 500 V and on the MΩ range, the insulation resistance L-cpc would be measured and the result recorded. One lead would then be connected to the neutral conductor and the other to the cpc, and the N-cpc resistance would be tested and the result recorded. Finally, the instrument leads would be connected to the line and neutral conductors and the L-N insulation resistance measured and the result recorded. Provided that the values obtained were greater than 2.0 MΩ the circuit would meet the requirements, however as this is a new circuit I would expect the value to be in excess of 200 MΩ.

This answer and similar variations are perfectly acceptable and you would obtain the marks for the question. However, it does rely on the procedure being written down correctly the first time without missing any steps. It involves a considerable amount of writing and it is often difficult to spot any errors during the examination when you read back through your answer.

Option 2

The answer can be structured as a set of bullet points, as follows.

- Prepare the cable for termination at the distribution board
- Ensure that any voltage sensitive or electronic devices are linked out or removed to prevent damage during the test
- Select an insulation resistance test instrument
- Check that calibration is current, leads are in good condition, batteries are OK and the instrument is functioning
- Set the instrument to the MΩ scale at 500 V
- Connect the instrument leads to the line and cpc at the db
- Test insulation resistance and record result
- Repeat with the instrument connected L to N and then N to cpc and record results
- Minimum acceptable value for each test is 2.0 MΩ but expect more than 200 MΩ as new circuit

There is plenty of space in the answer book, so you can leave a line between each bullet point, giving you the opportunity to add an additional line in later if you have missed a step in the process. You can also read through your answer much quicker and identify any omissions.

You will notice that there are some abbreviations used, such as 'db', 'L', 'N' and 'cpc'. The examiner will understand these when used in this context and it will not affect the marking for this question.

The second option, with the use of the bullet points, is generally quicker to complete, less prone to errors or omissions and clearly demonstrates your understanding of the test process. You can try both methods to find out which best suits you. However, Option 2 is **strongly recommended**.

Notes

Using diagrams

When answering questions use the best method for you to be able to provide the information required. If the question does not specifically ask for a drawing, but a drawing is a helpful way for you to answer, then use a drawing. For example, if the question asks how a ring final circuit continuity test is carried out, then the first stage is relatively easy to explain. When it comes to stages two and three, with the cross connection requirements, then using a drawing can save you a lot of time and writing.

Drawing a diagram like the one below is all that is required to explain the cross connection requirements for stage three of the test.

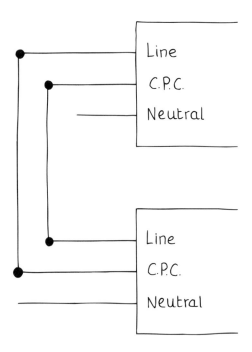

So, wherever it helps your explanation or saves a lot of writing, use a diagram or drawing to illustrate what you mean.

Tips from the examiners

✔ Remember, this is a closed book exam.

✔ Make the most of the course before you take the exam and be prepared to set time aside for revision before the exam.

✔ Allow enough time to get to the exam venue and try to allow yourself 30 minutes to settle in, complete your details on the answer book, and so on.

✔ Listen carefully to the instructions given by the invigilator.

✔ Take the time to read each question carefully before you answer. Do not rush – you should have plenty of time.

✔ Allow yourself approximately one hour to complete Section A (the first 20 questions) and the remaining hour and a half to complete the 6 questions in Section B.

✔ Attempt to answer every question.

✔ Remember to bring your calculator (a scientific one is useful) and a pen and pencils with you.

✔ You may find coloured pencils and a highlighter beneficial, to highlight relevant parts of the scenario, for instance.

✔ It is not essential to answer the questions in the order they appear on the paper. Just make sure that you mark each answer clearly with the correct number so that the examiner can identify each answer in relation to the corresponding question.

✔ If you have to continue an answer further on in the answer book, make sure that you indicate that it is continued elsewhere at the break in your answer.

Notes

Frequently asked questions

When can I sit the paper?

As this is a written examination, there are set exam dates. Your centre will tell you on what date you will be sitting the paper.

Can I use any reference books in the written test?

No, the exam is closed book so you are not allowed to take any books or reference materials in with you.

How many different parts of the written test are there?

There are two sections. Section A contains 20 questions, while Section B consists of 6 questions.

Do I have a time limit for taking the written exam?

You have two and a half hours to complete the test.

What grades of pass are there?

Pass or Fail.

When can I resit the test if I fail?

At the next available examination date following the receipt of your results, subject to centre agreement.

How long after the exam will I know the result?

Normally exam results are issued after 45 working days from the date of the examination.

How many times can I resit the exam?

Theoretically there is no limit to the number of times you can attempt the exam.

Exam content

The aim of Unit 301 is to enable you to develop the necessary technical knowledge and understanding about the inspection, testing and certification of electrical installations. There are three outcomes on which you will be tested in the written examination: preparation for inspection and testing, inspection, and testing.

Outcome 1 – Preparation for inspection and testing

You are required to be able to:
1.1   State the need for and the purpose of initial verification and periodic inspection and testing
1.2   State the information required to correctly conduct the inspection and testing of an installation
1.3   State the statutory and non-statutory requirements and relevant guidance material that apply to the activity of inspecting and testing of electrical installations
1.4   State the need to comply with statutory and non-statutory requirements, and guidance material for particular locations and environments in which electrical installations are installed
1.5   State the information to be contained on certificates and inspection reports and how the information is recorded on all certificates as indicated in BS 7671 (17th Edition).

Outcome 2 – Inspection

You are required to be able to:
2.1   State the human senses that may need to be employed during the inspection of an installation
2.2   Refer to and identify the items to be checked during the inspection process for given systems and locations as detailed in BS 7671 (17th Edition)
2.3   State the particular requirements for a periodic inspection of an electrical installation as defined in BS 7671 (17th Edition)
2.4   State the need to establish the extent and limitation of a Periodic Inspection Report, with the client and any relevant third parties, prior to commencing the inspection, and the need to record these details on the Periodic Inspection Report

2.5 State the requirements of the Electricity at Work Regulations for safe inspection and testing in terms of those:
   a   carrying out the work
   b   using the installation and the building during the inspection and testing.

Outcome 3 – Testing

For each topic, you are required to be able to:

Instruments

3.1 State the need for instruments to be regularly checked, and the need for their compliance with the requirements of BS 7671 (17th Edition) and HSE Guidance Note GS38

3.2 List the correct instruments, their characteristics and the appropriate scale to carry out each test, and explain the reasons for each choice

Sequence

3.3 State the recommended sequence of tests and the reasons for that sequence

Protective conductors

3.4 State the requirements which need to be considered for protective conductors in terms of:
   a   earthing conductors
   b   main protective bonding conductors
   c   supplementary protective bonding conductors
   d   circuit protective conductors

3.5 Describe the need for, and methods of verifying, the continuity of protective conductors and the interpretation of results

3.6 State the relationship between conductor length, csa and resistance

3.7 State the effect of temperature on a conductor

Ring circuits

3.8 State the effect on measured resistance when cables are connected in parallel

3.9 Describe the need for, and methods of, verifying the continuity of ring final circuit conductors and the interpretation of results

Insulation resistance

3.10 Explain, by example, the effect on insulation resistance and test results of:
   a   cables connected in parallel
   b   variation in cable length

3.11 Compare the differences between measurements taken for insulation resistance and conductor resistance, stating the order of magnitude that would be expected in each case

3.12 State the preconditions required for the performance of insulation testing

3.13 State the precautions to be taken before testing insulation resistance

3.14 Describe methods of testing insulation resistance

3.15 State the required test voltages and minimum values of insulation resistance for installations operating at various voltages

3.16 State the particular requirements for insulation resistance testing of circuits incorporating surge protection devices (SPDs) or sensitive electronic devices, to include disconnection and the test voltage to be applied where disconnection cannot be achieved

Electrical separation/SELV

3.17 Describe the tests to verify the separation of SELV circuits

3.18 State the particular requirements for protection by electrical separation (not SELV)

Special installations and locations

3.19 Describe the requirements for circuits in prescribed special installations and locations, by:
   a identifying the installations and locations to which special requirements apply
   b demonstrating the ability to make reference to the appropriate requirements in each case
   c identifying the requirements in relation to specific areas and installations from given information

IP code

3.20 State the appropriate minimum degree of protection required for given applications, as identified within the IP classification BS EN 60529

Polarity

3.21 Describe the need for and methods of testing used to identify correct polarity

Earth electrodes

3.22 Differentiate between the requirements for testing of earth electrodes for RCD-protected TT systems and electrodes for transformers and generators

Notes

Earth fault loop impedance

3.23 Describe the earth fault loop impedance paths for the following systems:

a TN-S

b TN-C-S

c TT

3.24 Describe methods of determining earth fault loop impedance in terms of:

a the tests used for measuring actual earth fault loop impedance

b methods of calculation of earth fault loop impedance from given data and measurement of conductor impedance

3.25 Given maximum tabulated values of earth fault loop impedance, verify that measured values are acceptable, taking into account conductor operating and ambient temperatures

Residual current devices (RCCBs/RCBOs)

3.26 Describe methods of testing the correct operation of RCDs, independent of in-built test facilities

3.27 State the applications for various RCD ratings

Prospective fault current

3.28 Describe methods of determining prospective fault current in terms of:

a prospective short-circuit current

b prospective earth fault current

3.29 Explain the importance of selecting protective devices appropriate to the prospective fault current

Phase sequence

3.30 Describe the requirements for checking phase sequence in terms of:

a the purpose of checking correct phase sequence

b test methods used to check phase rotation

Voltage drop

3.31 Describe the methods of verifying voltage drop compliance with BS 7671 in terms of measuring circuit impedance and calculation.

Exam practice 1

Exam practice 1

Sample test 1

The sample exam paper below has 26 questions, the same number as the written examination, and its structure follows that of the exam. The test appears first without answers, so you can use it as a mock exam. It is then repeated with worked-through answers and comments.

Answer the questions on some blank sheets of paper and try to time yourself.

General instructions
This examination consists of two sections.

Section A – 20 short-answer questions, each carrying three marks. Candidates must answer **all twenty** questions. It is recommended that candidates allow approximately one hour for this section.

Section B – Structured questions, each carrying 15 marks. Candidates must answer **all six** questions. It is recommended that candidates allow approximately 1½ hours for this section.

Section A
All questions carry equal marks. Answer **all twenty** questions.

1   State the **three** areas of responsibility that require a signature on an Electrical Installation Certificate.   (3 marks)

2   State **three** essential areas of information relating to the supply characteristics and earthing arrangements that must be completed on an Electrical Installation Certificate.   (3 marks)

3   State **three** non-statutory documents, other than BS 7671, which may be relevant to the inspection and testing process. (3 marks)

4   State **three** provisions for basic protection (direct contact) that may need to be inspected in a domestic installation.   (3 marks)

5   State the purpose of a periodic inspection and test of an electrical installation as defined in BS 7671.   (3 marks)

6   State **one** instrument used for **each** of the following tests.
   a)   Continuity of protective bonding conductors   (1 mark)
   b)   Earth electrode resistance for a TT installation   (1 mark)
   c)   Live polarity   (1 mark)

7   State, in the correct sequence, the first **three** tests to be carried out on a new ring final circuit.   (3 marks)

8   State the effect on conductor resistance when
   a)   cable length increases   (1 mark)
   b)   conductor temperature decreases   (1 mark)
   c)   cross-sectional area increases.   (1 mark)

9   State **three** factors that affect the values of insulation resistance for an electrical installation.   (3 marks)

10 State the test voltages required to test insulation resistance on a circuit operating at
   a)   25 V   (1 mark)
   b)   200 V   (1 mark)
   c)   600 V.   (1 mark)

11 State the minimum IP rating that applies to a distribution board when considering
   a)   the accessible horizontal top surface   (1 mark)
   b)   an intermediate barrier   (1 mark)
   c)   the vertical surfaces.   (1 mark)

12 State
   a)   **two** methods of carrying out a polarity test on a radial socket-outlet circuit before energising   (2 marks)
   b)   **one** item of equipment which may not require testing for polarity.   (1 mark)

13 a) State the difference in the earth electrode resistances for electrodes used to provide an earth for
   i) supply transformers (1 mark)
   ii) a TT installation protected by an RCD. (1 mark)
 b) State the significance of the value in a) ii) above when selecting the residual current setting of an RCD. (1 mark)

14 State a type of public supply system that contains
 a) a PEN conductor (1 mark)
 b) an installation earth electrode (1 mark)
 c) a distributor's separate protective conductor. (1 mark)

15 The measured values of R_1 and R_2 for a circuit are 0.37 Ω and 0.61 Ω respectively, and the Z_e for the installation is 0.2 Ω.
 a) Determine Z_S for the circuit, showing all calculations. (2 marks)
 b) State, giving reasons, how the measured Z_S may differ from the calculated value. (1 mark)

16 Determine whether the following measured values of Z_S are acceptable. Show **all** calculations.

	BS 7671 Max Z_S	**Measured Z_S**	
a)	1.44 Ω	0.8 Ω	(1 mark)
b)	0.72 Ω	0.66 Ω	(1 mark)
c)	0.36 Ω	0.21 Ω	(1 mark)

17 State the maximum rating for an RCD used for
 a) protection against fire in an agricultural installation (1 mark)
 b) additional protection (1 mark)
 c) a caravan supply socket in a caravan park. (1 mark)

18 Determine the maximum operating current, in milli-amperes, for an RCD providing fault protection (indirect contact) for a domestic TT installation, if the installation earth electrode resistance (R_A) is 166 Ω. Show **all** calculations. (3 marks)

19 State
  a) the **two** tests required to determine the prospective
      fault current for a single-phase installation   (2 marks)
  b) which of the results obtained in a) above is recorded
      on an Electrical Installation Certificate.   (1 mark)

20 A new circuit for an immersion heater is protected by a
   BS EN 60898 circuit-breaker. State **three** functional checks
   that would need to be carried out on this circuit.   (3 marks)

Section B

Questions 21 to 26 refer to the following scenario. Answer **all six** questions. All questions carry equal marks.
Please show all calculations.

A periodic inspection is to be carried out on a residence, with gardens front and rear, which is to be used by a housing association for residential letting.

The original installation was carried out ten years ago, and a kitchen and bathroom extension was added five years later when mains gas was installed to the property. There are no forms of certification or circuit details available for the original installation or the additional work.

The installation forms part of a 230 V, 50 Hz TT system with a PFC of 1.3 kA. A 100 mA RCD, which also serves as the main isolator, is installed in the consumer unit.

The means of terminating the earthing conductor at the installation earth electrode is by the use of an exposed clamp, located above ground level.

For the purpose of answering the following questions, details of the installation have been provided in **Figure 1**.

Values of conductor resistance are given in **Figure 2**.

Figure 1

Consumer unit					
Circuit	Designation	Circuit-breaker BS EN 60898 Type B	Cable details	Cable length	BS 7671 maximum Z_S
1	Shower	40 A	Line 6.0 mm² CPC 2.5 mm²	25 m	1.15 Ω
2	Downstairs power (Ring circuit)	32 A	Line 2.5 mm² CPC 1.5 mm²	60 m	1.44 Ω
3	Upstairs power (Ring circuit)	32 A	Line 2.5 mm² CPC 1.5 mm²	75 m	1.44 Ω
4	Cooker	32 A	Line 4.0 mm² CPC 1.5 mm²	12 m	1.44 Ω
5	Upstairs lights	6 A	Line 1.5 mm² CPC 1.0 mm²	50 m	7.67 Ω
6	Downstairs lights	6 A	Line 1.5 mm² CPC 1.0 mm²	40 m	7.67 Ω
7	Boiler	10 A	Line 1.5 mm² CPC 1.0 mm²	10 m	4.60 Ω
8	Spare				

Figure 2

CSA in mm²	Resistance in mΩ/m
1.0	18.1
1.5	12.1
2.5	7.41
4.0	4.61
6.0	3.08
10.0	1.83
25.0	0.727

21 List
   a) the documents that are to be issued to the client on
       completion of the periodic inspection and test   (3 marks)
   b) **two** statutory and **three** non-statutory publications
       that are relevant to the periodic inspection and
       testing process   (5 marks)
   c) the persons who should be consulted to establish the
       extent and limitation of the periodic inspection and test (2 marks)
   d) **five** supply characteristics required by the inspector in
       order to carry out the inspection and test.   (5 marks)

22 It has been agreed that a full periodic inspection and test is
   to be undertaken.
   a) List **two** of the human senses that would be used during
       the inspection giving an example of the use of **each**. (4 marks)
   b) List the test instrument and the appropriate scale to
       be used for testing each of the following:
       i)   continuity of protective conductors
       ii)   insulation resistance
       iii) earth fault loop impedance
       iv)   prospective fault current
       v)   operation of RCDs for additional protection.   (10 marks)
   c) State the guidance document specifically related to
       test equipment for use by electricians.   (1 mark)

23 a) A test of insulation resistance for individual circuits
       produced the following results:
           10 MΩ, 15 MΩ, 5 MΩ, 20 MΩ, 6 MΩ, 12 MΩ and 12 MΩ
       Determine the overall insulation resistance of the
       installation and whether this value meets the
       requirements of BS 7671. Show **all** calculations.   (10 marks)
   b) The outside lighting is controlled by a photo cell located
       near the apex of the gable end of the property. State
       what action would be required regarding the photo
       cell, before carrying out the insulation resistance test
       on this lighting circuit.   (2 marks)
   c) State the effect on insulation resistance of
       i)   an increase in cable length
       ii)   an increase in conductor cross-sectional area
       iii) additional cables connected in parallel.   (3 marks)

052888

24 a) Describe the test procedure to determine the resistance of the installation earth electrode. Detail should include:
   i) the preparation
   ii) safety requirements
   iii) test process
   iv) reinstating the installation. (9 marks)

b) A test of the main protective bonding conductors produced the following results:
   MET to gas 0.028 Ω, length 15 m
   MET to water 0.046 Ω, length 10 m
   Using the information in **Figure 2**, calculate the cross-sectional area of the conductor used for each of these services that would produce these test results. Show **all** calculations. (6 marks)

25 a) Describe, using a fully labelled diagram, the earth fault loop impedance path for the cooker circuit. (13 marks)

b) State, for the RCD, the
   i) purpose of the in-built test facility (1 mark)
   ii) recommended period for testing using the in-built test facility. (1 mark)

26 State
   a) the purpose for which this periodic inspection and test is required, as identified on the report (2 marks)
   b) the maximum recommended interval between periodic inspections for residential accommodation (2 marks)
   c) **two** observations, together with the appropriate recommendations, using code 1, 2, 3 or 4, which should be recorded in the 'observations and recommendations' of the report (4 marks)
   d) **one** appropriate remedial action for **each** of the observations given in c) above (6 marks)
   e) whether the Schedule of Inspections item 'particular protective measures for special installations and locations' is applicable and give a reason. (1 mark)

Questions and answers

The questions in sample test 1 are repeated below with sample answers, and comments and advice where appropriate.

Section A

1   State the **three** areas of responsibility that require a
    signature on an Electrical Installation Certificate.   (3 marks)

Answer
- Design   (1 mark)
- Construction   (1 mark)
- Inspection and testing   (1 mark)

Comments
An acceptable alternative answer to construction is installation.

Examiner's tip: Remember, when the question asks you to 'state' something then all you need to do is write the answer, even if it is only one word. There is no need to write a full sentence.

2   State **three** essential areas of information relating to the
    supply characteristics and earthing arrangements that must
    be completed on an Electrical Installation Certificate.   (3 marks)

Answer
- Earthing arrangements   (1 mark)
- Number and type of live conductors   (1 mark)
- Nature of supply parameters   (1 mark)

Comments
Any three essential areas of information could be chosen from the following list:
- earthing arrangements
- number and type of live conductors
- nature of supply parameters
- supply protective device characteristics.

The supply characteristics and earthing arrangements section of the Electrical Installation Certificate, which must be completed, is shown below.

Notes

SUPPLY CHARACTERISTICS AND EARTHING ARRANGEMENTS	Tick boxes and enter details, as appropriate		
Earthing arrangements	**Number and Type of Live Conductors**	**Nature of Supply Parameters**	**Supply Protective Device Characteristics**
TN-C ☐ TN-S ☐ TN-C-S ☐ TT ☐ IT ☐ Alternative source ☐ of supply (to be detailed on attached schedules)	a.c. ☐ d.c. ☐ 1-phase, 2-wire ☐ 2-pole ☐ 2-phase, 3-wire ☐ 3-pole ☐ 3-phase, 3-wire ☐ other ☐ 3-phase, 4-wire ☐	Nominal voltage, U/U_0 (1) .... V Nominal frequency, f (1) .... Hz Prospective fault current, I_{pf} (2) .... kA External loop impedance, Z_e (2) .... Ω *(Note: (1) by enquiry, (2) by enquiry or by measurement)*	Type: .... Rated current...............A

From the *IEE Wiring Regulations*, page 333

3 State **three** non-statutory documents, other than BS 7671, which may be relevant to the inspection and testing process.   (3 marks)

Answer
- Guidance Note 3   (1 mark)
- GS38   (1 mark)
- On-Site Guide   (1 mark)

Comments
Non-statutory documents are those that you are not legally bound to follow, but which provide advice and guidance on a variety of activities. Those that provide specific guidance on the inspection and testing process are listed above.

A statutory document, for example the Electricity at Work Regulations 1989, is one that must be complied with by law.

4   State three provisions for basic protection (direct contact) that may need to be inspected in a domestic installation.   (3 marks)

Answer
- Insulation   (1 mark)
- Barriers and enclosures   (1 mark)
- SELV   (1 mark)

Comments
BS 7671 requires that provision for basic protection (direct contact) is provided by one or more of the following methods:
- insulation of live parts
- installation of barriers or enclosures
- obstacles
- placing out of reach
- SELV or PELV
- double insulation
- reinforced insulation.

However, obstacles, placing out of reach, double insulation and reinforced insulation would not normally be considered acceptable for a domestic installation and would not gain you any marks.

5   State the purpose of a periodic inspection and test of an electrical installation as defined in BS 7671.   (3 marks)

Answer
To establish whether the installation is in a safe condition for continued service.   (3 marks)

Comments
Any explanation that indicates that the purpose of an inspection and test is to ensure that the electrical installation is satisfactory for continued service would be acceptable.

Part 6 of BS 7671 requires that the periodic inspection and testing of an electrical installation shall be carried out to determine, so far as is reasonably practicable, whether the installation is in a satisfactory condition for continued service.

6 State **one** instrument used for **each** of the following tests.
   a) Continuity of protective bonding conductors   (1 mark)
   b) Earth electrode resistance for a TT installation   (1 mark)
   c) Live polarity   (1 mark)

Answer
   a) Low-resistance ohmmeter   (1 mark)
   b) Earth fault loop impedance tester   (1 mark)
   c) Approved voltage indicator   (1 mark)

Comments
   b) An acceptable alternative to answer b would be an earth electrode
       resistance tester.

   c) An acceptable alternative to answer c would be any instrument that
       meets the requirements of GS38 and indicates live polarity, for
       example an earth fault loop impedance tester.

7 State, in the correct sequence, the first **three** tests to be
   carried out on a new ring final circuit.   (3 marks)

Answer
   • Continuity of protective conductors
   • Continuity of ring final circuit conductors
   • Insulation resistance   (3 marks)

Comments
The above list is given in the correct sequence, as identified in BS 7671.

A suitable alternative answer would be:
   • continuity of ring final circuit conductors
   • insulation resistance
   • earth fault loop impedance.
This alternative is acceptable since a satisfactory continuity of ring final
circuit test includes confirmation of continuity of protective conductors
and polarity.

Examiner's tip: If the sequence is given in the incorrect order or an
inappropriate test is included then **no** marks will be awarded. The
question specifically asks for the correct sequence.

Notes

8   State the effect on conductor resistance when
    a)   cable length increases   (1 mark)
    b)   conductor temperature decreases   (1 mark)
    c)   cross-sectional area increases.   (1 mark)

Answer
    a)   Increase   (1 mark)
    b)   Decrease   (1 mark)
    c)   Decrease   (1 mark)

Comments
Examiner's tip: The above answers are suitable for this question and
there is no need to write anything more. However, if values were given
in the question, then a calculation and a value would be required as part
of the answer.

9   State **three** factors that affect the values of insulation
    resistance for an electrical installation.   (3 marks)

Answer
    •   Length of circuits   (1 mark)
    •   Number of circuits connected in parallel   (1 mark)
    •   Condition of the installation   (1 mark)

Comments
The following factors could affect the condition of the installation:
    •   damage
    •   wear and tear
    •   excessive electrical loading
    •   aging
    •   environmental influences.
Any one of these would be an acceptable alternative answer to 'condition
of the installation'.

10 State the test voltages required to test insulation resistance
    on a circuit operating at
    a)   25 V   (1 mark)
    b)   200 V   (1 mark)
    c)   600 V.   (1 mark)

Answer
    a)   250 V   (1 mark)
    b)   500 V   (1 mark)
    c)   1000 V   (1 mark)

Comments

The appropriate test voltages from BS 7671 are shown in the table below.

Notes

Table 61   Minimum values of insulation resistance

Circuit nominal voltage (V)	Test voltage d.c. (V)	Minimum insulation resistance (MΩ)
SELV and PELV	250	≥ 0.5
Up to and including 500 V with the exception of the above systems	500	≥ 1.0
Above 500 V	1000	≥ 1.0

From the *IEE Wiring Regulations*, Table 61, page 158

11 State the minimum IP rating that applies to a distribution
   board when considering
   a)   the accessible horizontal top surface   (1 mark)
   b)   an intermediate barrier   (1 mark)
   c)   the vertical surfaces.   (1 mark)

Answer
   a)   IP4X   (1 mark)
   b)   IP2X   (1 mark)
   c)   IP2X   (1 mark)

Comments

An acceptable alternative for answer a would be IPXXD, and an
acceptable alternative for answers b and c would be IPXXB.

BS 7671 states that:
   • the horizontal top surface of a barrier or an enclosure which is
     readily accessible shall provide a degree of protection of at least
     IPXXD or IP4X
   • an intermediate barrier shall be provided to prevent contact with a
     live part, such a barrier affording a degree of protection of at least
     IPXXB or IP2X and removable only by the use of a tool
   • live parts shall be inside enclosures or behind barriers providing at
     least the degree of protection IPXXB or IP2X.

Notes

12 State

a) **two** methods of carrying out a polarity test on a radial socket-outlet circuit before energising (2 marks)

b) **one** item of equipment which may not require testing for polarity. (1 mark)

Answer

a)
- Using the $R_1 + R_2$ test (1 mark)
- The use of a long lead (1 mark)

b) Insulated ES lampholders (1 mark)

Comments

b) A suitable alternative for answer b would be to make reference to certain types of E14 and E27 lampholders.

13 a) State the difference in the earth electrode resistances for electrodes used to provide an earth for

i) supply transformers (1 mark)

ii) a TT installation protected by an RCD. (1 mark)

b) State the significance of the value in a) ii) above when selecting the residual current setting of an RCD. (1 mark)

Answer

a) i) Should not exceed 20 Ω (1 mark)

ii) Recommended below 200 Ω (1 mark)

b) $\dfrac{50}{R_A} = I_{\Delta n}$ (1 mark)

Comments

a) i) Distributors usually state that the earth electrode at a supply transformer will not be in excess of 20 Ω.

ii) BS 7671 advises that the resistance of the installation earth electrode should be as low as possible. Both BS 7671 and Guidance Note 3 recommend that values of earth electrode resistance above 200 Ω require further investigation, as they may not be stable.

14 State a type of public supply system that contains
   a)   a PEN conductor   (1 mark)
   b)   an installation earth electrode   (1 mark)
   c)   a distributor's separate protective conductor.   (1 mark)

Answer
   a)   TN-C-S   (1 mark)
   b)   TT   (1 mark)
   c)   TN-S   (1 mark)

Comments
Stating TN-C for answer a, and IT for answer b would not be acceptable since these are not generally either available or permissable on the public supply system.

15 The measured values of R_1 and R_2 for a circuit are 0.37 Ω and 0.61 Ω respectively, and the Z_e for the installation is 0.2 Ω.
   a)   Determine Z_S for the circuit, showing all calculations.   (2 marks)
   b)   State, giving reasons, how the measured Z_S may differ from the calculated value.   (1 mark)

Answer
   a) $Z_S = Z_e + (R_1 + R_2)$
       $Z_S = 0.2 + (0.37 + 0.61)$ (1 mark)
       $Z_S = 1.18\,\Omega$ (1 mark)
   b) Z_S test will include parallel paths whilst the values of Z_e and $R_1 + R_2$ may not.   (1 mark)

Comments
Examiner's tip: When carrying out calculations, show all steps to ensure full marks.

16 Determine whether the following measured values of Z_S are acceptable. Show **all** calculations.

	BS 7671 Max Z_S	Measured Z_S	
a)	1.44 Ω	0.8 Ω	(1 mark)
b)	0.72 Ω	0.66 Ω	(1 mark)
c)	0.36 Ω	0.21 Ω	(1 mark)

Answer

a)	0.8 x 1.44 Ω = 1.152 Ω	> 0.8 Ω	Acceptable	(1 mark)
b)	0.8 x 0.72 Ω = 0.576 Ω	< 0.66 Ω	Not acceptable	(1 mark)
c)	0.8 x 0.36 Ω = 0.288 Ω	> 0.21 Ω	Acceptable	(1 mark)

Comments

As no additional information has been provided, the simple method of determining compliance identified in Appendix 14 of BS 7671 is used. The measured Z_S should not exceed 0.8 multiplied by the maximum permitted Z_S.

17 State the maximum rating for an RCD used for

a)	protection against fire in an agricultural installation	(1 mark)
b)	additional protection	(1 mark)
c)	a caravan supply socket in a caravan park.	(1 mark)

Answer

a)	300 mA	(1 mark)
b)	30 mA	(1 mark)
c)	30 mA	(1 mark)

18 Determine the maximum operating current, in milli-amperes, for an RCD providing fault protection (indirect contact) for a domestic TT installation, if the installation earth electrode resistance (R_A) is 166 Ω. Show **all** calculations.   (3 marks)

Answer

$R_A \times I_{\Delta n} \leq 50$

$\dfrac{50}{R_A} = I_{\Delta n}$ (1 mark)

$\dfrac{50}{166} = 0.3\ A$ (1 mark)

So, maximum = 300 mA   (1 mark)

Comments

Examiner's tip: When carrying out calculations, show all steps to ensure full marks.

19 State

a)   the **two** tests required to determine the prospective fault current for a single-phase installation (2 marks)

b)   which of the results obtained in a) above is recorded on an Electrical Installation Certificate. (1 mark)

Answer

a)   Prospective earth fault current and prospective short-circuit current. (2 marks)

b)   The greater of the two values. (1 mark)

Comments

Acceptable alternative answers would be:

a)   Line to earth (L–E) fault current and line to neutral (L–N) fault current.

b)   The highest of the two values in answer a is recorded as the prospective fault current (I_{pf}).

20 A new circuit for an immersion heater is protected by a BS EN 60898 circuit-breaker. State **three** functional checks that would need to be carried out on this circuit. (3 marks)

Answer

- Switching of the circuit-breaker (1 mark)
- Correct operation of the local switch (1 mark)
- Correct operation of thermostat (1 mark)

Comments

Suitable alternative answers could include correct operation of other equipment, such as operation of timers and checking that the heater worked correctly (heated up).

Section B

21 List
  a) the documents that are to be issued to the client on completion of the periodic inspection and test   (3 marks)
  b) **two** statutory and **three** non-statutory publications that are relevant to the periodic inspection and testing process   (5 marks)
  c) the persons who should be consulted to establish the extent and limitation of the periodic inspection and test   (2 marks)
  d) **five** supply characteristics required by the inspector in order to carry out the inspection and test.   (5 marks)

Answer

a)
  • Periodic Inspection Report   (1 mark)
  • Schedule of Inspections   (1 mark)
  • Schedule of Test Results   (1 mark)

b) **Statutory**
  • The Electricity at Work Regulations   (1 mark)
  • The Health & Safety at Work Act   (1 mark)
  Non-statutory
  • BS 7671   (1 mark)
  • GS38   (1 mark)
  • Guidance Note 3   (1 mark)

c)
  • The owner   (1 mark)
  • The housing association   (1 mark)

d)
  • Earthing arrangements   (1 mark)
  • Number and type of live conductors   (1 mark)
  • Supply voltage   (1 mark)
  • Supply frequency   (1 mark)
  • Prospective fault current   (1 mark)

Comments

a) The abbreviation PIR (for Periodic Inspection Report) would be acceptable. However, incorrect document titles or form numbers would not be acceptable. Listing irrelevant documents will result in no marks being awarded; where specific documents are requested, a general list of all documents is not an acceptable answer.

b) A suitable alternative for the non-statutory documents would be the On-Site Guide or the Memorandum of Guidance on the Electricity at Work Regulations.
Examiner's tip: When answering the question, clearly indicate which documents are statutory and which are non-statutory.

c) The inspector may need to consult with a number of people. In this case, the owner of the property and the housing association would need to be involved. Consultation with the client, and/or the client's representative and other interested parties, prior to the periodic inspection and testing being carried out, is essential to determine the extent and limitations. This will include the degree of disconnection that will be acceptable.

d) Suitable alternative answers include:
- external loop impedance (Z_e)
- supply protective device characteristics.

The table below shows the information required from the model Periodic Inspection Report in BS 7671.

SUPPLY CHARACTERISTICS AND EARTHING ARRANGEMENTS	Tick boxes and enter details, as appropriate		
Earthing arrangements	**Number and Type of Live Conductors**	**Nature of Supply Parameters**	**Supply Protective Device Characteristics**
TN-C ☐ TN-S ☐ TN-C-S ☐ TT ☐ IT ☐	a.c. ☐ d.c. ☐ 1-phase, 2-wire ☐ 2-pole ☐	Nominal voltage, U/U_0 [(1)] .... V Nominal frequency, f [(1)] .... Hz	Type: ....
	2-phase, 3-wire ☐ 3-pole ☐	Prospective fault current, I_{pf} [(2)] .... kA	Rated current..............A
Alternative source ☐ of supply (to be detailed on attached schedules)	3-phase, 3-wire ☐ other ☐ 3-phase, 4-wire ☐	External loop impedance, Z_e [(2)] .... Ω *(Note: (1) by enquiry, (2) by enquiry or by measurement)*	

From the *IEE Wiring Regulations*, page 333

Notes

22 It has been agreed that a full periodic inspection and test is to be undertaken.

a) List **two** of the human senses that would be used during the inspection giving an example of the use of **each**. (4 marks)

b) List the test instrument and the appropriate scale to be used for testing each of the following:
   i) continuity of protective conductors
   ii) insulation resistance
   iii) earth fault loop impedance
   iv) prospective fault current
   v) operation of RCDs for additional protection. (10 marks)

c) State the guidance document specifically related to test equipment for use by electricians. (1 mark)

Answer

a)
- Sight (identify missing labels) (2 marks)
- Touch (identify loose terminals) (2 marks)

b) i) Low-resistance ohmmeter set to low ohms (2 marks)
   ii) Insulation resistance tester set to $M\Omega$ (2 marks)
   iii) Earth fault loop impedance tester set to 200 Ω (2 marks)
   iv) Prospective fault current tester set to kA (2 marks)
   v) RCD test instrument indicating ms (2 marks)

c) GS38 (1 mark)

Comments

a) Suitable alternatives would be:
- smell (to detect the smell of burning or overheating)
- hearing (to detect the sound of arcing created by a poorly terminated conductor within an enclosure).

Any suitable use of the senses should receive marks.

b) Although multifunction, auto-ranging test instruments may be in common use, the answer requires the correct function and appropriate scale to be stated in each case.

23 a) A test of insulation resistance for individual circuits produced   **Notes**
the following results:
10 MΩ, 15 MΩ, 5 MΩ, 20 MΩ, 6 MΩ, 12 MΩ and 12 MΩ
Determine the overall insulation resistance of the installation
and whether this value meets the requirements of BS 7671.
Show **all** calculations.   (10 marks)

b) The outside lighting is controlled by a photo cell located
near the apex of the gable end of the property. State
what action would be required regarding the photo cell,
before carrying out the insulation resistance test on this
lighting circuit.   (2 marks)

c) State the effect on insulation resistance of
i)   an increase in cable length
ii)   an increase in conductor cross-sectional area
iii) additional cables connected in parallel.   (3 marks)

Answer

a) $\dfrac{1}{R_t} = \dfrac{1}{R_1} + \dfrac{1}{R_2} + \dfrac{1}{R_3} + \dfrac{1}{R_4} + \dfrac{1}{R_5} + \dfrac{1}{R_6} + \dfrac{1}{R_7}$ (1 mark)

$\dfrac{1}{R_t} = \dfrac{1}{10} + \dfrac{1}{15} + \dfrac{1}{5} + \dfrac{1}{20} + \dfrac{1}{6} + \dfrac{1}{12} + \dfrac{1}{12}$ (1 mark)

$\dfrac{1}{R_t} = 0.1 + 0.067 + 0.2 + 0.05 + 0.167 + 0.083 + 0.083$ (2 marks)

$\dfrac{1}{R_t} = 0.75$ (1 mark)

$R_t = \dfrac{1}{0.75}$ (2 marks)

$R_t = 1.33\ \text{M}\Omega$ (1 mark)

As 1.33 MΩ $\geq$ 1 MΩ this is acceptable.   (2 marks)

b) The photo cell will need to be disconnected and linked out. (2 marks)

c) i)   Decrease   (1 mark)
ii)   None   (1 mark)
iii) Decrease   (1 mark)

Notes

Comments

a) Examiner's tip: Show all calculations for each step.

b) An acceptable alternative answer would be: link line and neutral and test between the linked conductors and earth and record a limitation on the schedule of test results for the test between live conductors. If the photo cell is just disconnected the circuit will be broken and therefore not completely tested, therefore it must be linked or shorted out.

c) Examiner's tip: Make sure you read the question, as in this case it is easy to confuse insulation resistance with conductor resistance.

24 a) Describe the test procedure to determine the resistance of the installation earth electrode. Detail should include:
  i)   the preparation
  ii)   safety requirements
  iii) test process
  iv)   reinstating the installation.   (9 marks)

b) A test of the main protective bonding conductors produced the following results:
    MET to gas 0.028 Ω, length 15 m
    MET to water 0.046 Ω, length 10 m
  Using the information in **Figure 2**, calculate the cross-sectional area of the conductor used for each of these services that would produce these test results. Show **all** calculations.   (6 marks)

Answer

a) • Seek permission to isolate the installation   (1 mark)
   • Safely isolate supply and all circuit-breakers   (1 mark)
   • Select an earth fault loop impedance tester, confirm
     calibration, condition and leads to GS38   (1 mark)
   • Disconnect the earthing conductor from the main
     earthing terminal   (1 mark)
   • Connect the instrument, earth lead to disconnected
     earthing conductor, neutral to outgoing neutral of main
     isolator and phase to outgoing phase of main isolator   (1 mark)
   • Close the main isolator   (1 mark)
   • Check the instrument set to 200 Ω and carry out the
     test and record the result   (1 mark)
   • Open the main isolator and disconnect instrument
     in the reverse order   (1 mark)
   • Reconnect the earthing conductor   (1 mark)

b) **Gas**

Ohms per metre = resistance ÷ length

Ω/m = $\underline{0.028}$ (1 mark)
       15

     = 0.0018 Ω/m   (1 mark)

     = 1.8 mΩ/m = 10 mm^2   (1 mark)

Water

Ohms per metre = resistance ÷ length

Ω/m = $\underline{0.046}$ (1 mark)
       10

     = 0.0046 Ω/m   (1 mark)

     = 4.6 mΩ/m = 4 mm^2   (1 mark)

Comments

a) From reading the scenario, the installation is TT and this lends itself to the test using an earth fault loop impedance tester. A suitable alternative would be a full description using an earth electrode resistance tester.

Examiner's tip: Use of short statements and bullet points makes it easier to produce a full description, and is less time-consuming. Remember, you have one minute for each mark.

b) Examiner's tip: The answer could be found by multiplying each value in the table by the length of the conductor and matching this against the test result. This can be a very time-consuming process, and so would not be recommended due to the time constraints. However, an answer established in this way would be acceptable.

Notes

25 a) Describe, using a fully labelled diagram, the earth fault loop impedance path for the cooker circuit. (13 marks)

   b) State, for the RCD, the

   i) purpose of the in-built test facility (1 mark)

   ii) recommended period for testing using the in-built test facility. (1 mark)

Answer

a)

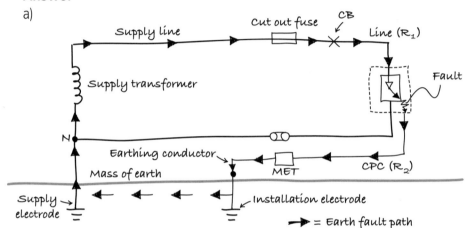

(6 marks for the diagram)
(7 marks for labelling)

   b) i) Checks mechanical operation (1 mark)

   ii) Quarterly (1 mark)

Comments

a) If the system drawn is not that required for the scenario (in this case TT), no marks will be awarded.

Examiner's tip: Make sure you refer to the scenario when drawing the earth fault loop impedance path to ensure you show the correct system.

			Notes

26 State

   a)   the purpose for which this periodic inspection and test is required, as identified on the report   (2 marks)

   b)   the maximum recommended interval between periodic inspections for residential accommodation   (2 marks)

   c)   **two** observations, together with the appropriate recommendations, using code 1, 2, 3 or 4, which should be recorded in the 'observations and recommendations' of the report   (4 marks)

   d)   **one** appropriate remedial action for **each** of the observations given in c) above   (6 marks)

   e)   whether the Schedule of Inspections item 'particular protective measures for special installations and locations' is applicable and give a reason.   (1 mark)

Answer

   a)   Residential letting – change of occupancy   (2 marks)

   b)   Five years   (2 marks)

   c)   i)   Observation – no additional protection for socket-outlets   (1 mark)
            Recommendation – 2   (1 mark)

       ii)   Observation – Earthing conductor termination exposed   (1 mark)
            Recommendation – 2   (1 mark)

   d)   i)   Install RCBOs in place of the circuit-breakers protecting the socket-outlet circuits.   (3 marks)

       ii)   The connection of the earthing conductor to the earth electrode should be enclosed in a suitable earth-pit to protect against mechanical damage.   (3 marks)

   e)   Yes, because there is a bathroom.   (1 mark)

Notes

Comments

a) Suitable alternatives would be a housing association request or landlord's request.

b) Residential accommodation is five years, not to be confused with domestic installations, which is a maximum interval of ten years.

c) The two answers given for this question are clearly indicated in the scenario. Reading the scenario is extremely important.

d) Suitable alternatives would be: the inclusion of a 30 mA RCD to protect socket-outlet circuits, and suitable protection of the earthing conductor and electrode termination.
    Examiner's tip: In situations where an option is given in one part of a question, as in part c above, the answer provided may affect other parts of the question, for example part d above.

e) A suitable alternative would be: Yes, because a shower is installed. The scenario states the presence of a bathroom, and Figure 1 indicates a shower circuit.
    Examiner's tip: The reference to special installations and locations always refers to those identified in BS 7671, and not those indicated in Part P of the Building Regulations. However, some of the BS 7671 locations are duplicated in Part P.

Exam practice 2

Exam practice 2

Sample test 2

The sample exam paper below has 26 questions, the same number as the written examination, and its structure follows that of the exam. The test appears first without answers, so you can use it as a mock exam. It is then repeated with worked-through answers and comments.

Answer the questions on some blank sheets of paper and try to time yourself.

General instructions
This examination consists of two sections.

Section A – 20 short-answer questions, each carrying three marks. Candidates must answer **all twenty** questions. It is recommended that candidates allow approximately one hour for this section.

Section B – Structured questions, each carrying 15 marks. Candidates must answer **all six** questions. It is recommended that candidates allow approximately 1½ hours for this section.

Section A
All questions carry equal marks. Answer **all twenty** questions.

1 State
   a) **one** example of installation work that would require an Electrical Installation Certificate (1 mark)
   b) the persons that should retain copies of the certificate in a). (2 marks)

2 State the purpose of an initial verification of a newly installed circuit. (3 marks)

3 State **three** items that may be inspected, while carrying out an initial verification of an installation, when considering fault protection provided by automatic disconnection of supply. (3 marks)

4 a) List the **two** documents that must accompany a
        Periodic Inspection Report.   (2 marks)
   b) State **one** piece of information that must be written
        on a Periodic Inspection Report and agreed with the
        client prior to testing.   (1 mark)

5 During periodic inspection and testing of an installation
   the inspector must ensure the safety of persons. State
   three practical actions that the inspector can take in order
   to maintain a safe environment during this process.   (3 marks)

6 List **three** items of technical information which are to be
   entered on both an Electrical Installation Certificate and
   a Periodic Inspection Report.   (3 marks)

7 State **three** safety checks to be carried out on an earth
   fault loop impedance tester and leads prior to conducting
   a test on a lighting circuit.   (3 marks)

8 A test is to be conducted on an immersion heater circuit
   to establish the value of $R_1 + R_2$. State
   a) the instrument to be used   (1 mark)
   b) what action must be taken regarding the test leads
        to obtain an accurate result   (1 mark)
   c) the meaning of $R_1 + R_2$.   (1 mark)

9 A ring final circuit continuity test is to be carried out on a
   newly installed circuit. State
   a) the instrument to be used   (1 mark)
   b) **two** additional tests that are automatically carried out
        when completing this test.   (2 marks)

10 The insulation resistance of a three-phase installation is to
   be tested. State
   a) the conductors between which the test should be
        carried out   (2 marks)
   b) the units in which the test is measured.   (1 mark)

11 State
   a) **two** physical changes made to an installation that
       may result in an increase in the resistance of a
       circuit conductor   (2 marks)
   b) **one** reason, apart from a fault or deterioration,
       why overall insulation resistance of an installation
       may decrease.   (1 mark)

12 BS 7671 identifies protective measures to be used for
   electrical separation. State
   a) **two** methods of achieving basic protection for
       electrical separation   (2 marks)
   b) the method of providing fault protection for electrical
       separation.   (1 mark)

13 State
   a) the IP code verified by the use of
       (i)   1 mm diameter wire   (1 mark)
       (ii) the standard test finger   (1 mark)
   b) the meaning of 'X' in the code IPX4.   (1 mark)

14 Explain briefly why it is necessary to carry out a polarity
   test on a radial socket-outlet circuit.   (3 marks)

15 State
   a) **two** instruments that may be used when confirming
       the effectiveness of an earth electrode   (2 marks)
   b) what action must be taken with regard to the earthing
       conductor during the test.   (1 mark)

16 A test is to be conducted on an existing installation to
   establish the value of Z_e. State
   a) the instrument to be used   (1 mark)
   b) the action to be taken with regard to the
       i)   earthing conductor   (1 mark)
       ii) supply.   (1 mark)

Notes

17 The maximum tabulated values of earth loop impedance, given in BS 7671, for **three** circuits are 2.3 Ω, 1.44 Ω and 0.57 Ω. The measured values for these circuits are 1.22 Ω, 0.44 Ω and 0.36 Ω respectively. Determine if the measured values are acceptable. Show **all** calculations. (3 marks)

18 An RCD to BS EN 61008 is to provide additional protection for 13 A socket-outlets, for use by ordinary persons, intended for general use. State
   a) the maximum permitted operating current ($I_{\Delta n}$) of the RCD (1 mark)
   b) the maximum test current when testing the device in a) (1 mark)
   c) the maximum permitted disconnection time for the test in b). (1 mark)

19 List three types of installation where a 300 mA RCD would be installed because a particular risk of fire exists. (3 marks)

20 The prospective fault current at the origin of a 230 V single-phase installation forming part of a TN-S system is to be measured. State
   a) the conductors between which testing is to be carried out (2 marks)
   b) which result from a) is to be recorded on an Electrical Installation Certificate. (1 mark)

Section B

Questions 21 to 26 refer to the following scenario. Answer **all six** questions. All questions carry equal marks. **Show all calculations**.

The electrical installation within a new light industrial unit requires an initial verification. The metal-clad three-phase and neutral distribution board contains BS EN 61009 RCBOs for the socket-outlet circuits and BS EN 60898 circuit-breakers for all other circuits. The wiring system is thermoplastic (pvc) insulated single-core cables, with copper conductors, enclosed in pvc conduit and trunking throughout.

Each circuit has a copper cpc the same cross-sectional area (csa) as the circuit line conductor(s).

Figure 1 shows the necessary details of the installation circuits.
Figure 2 shows the conductor resistance values per metre.

Figure 1

Circuit designation			Protective device 10 kA BS EN 60898 BS EN 61009		Conductor csa (mm²)		Circuit length (m)
Way	Phase	Description	Type	Rating 1_n (A)	Live	cpc	
1	L1	Lathe	D	10	1.5	1.5	27
	L2						
	L3						
2	L1	Forge	D	10	1.5	1.5	25
	L2						
	L3						
3	L1	Workshop lighting	C	6	1.5	1.5	42
	L2	Workshop lighting	C	6	1.5	1.5	45
	L3	Workshop lighting	C	6	1.5	1.5	47
4	L1	Office, WC and store lighting	C	6	1.5	1.5	15
	L2	Socket to BS EN 60309	C	16/30 mA	2.5	2.5	18
	L3	Socket to BS EN 60309	C	16/30 mA	2.5	2.5	24
5	L1	Socket to BS EN 60309	C	16/30 mA	2.5	2.5	26
	L2	Spare	–	–	–	–	–
	L3	Spare	–	–	–	–	–
6	L1	Sockets in office	B	32/30 mA	4	4	20
	L2	Spare	–	–	–	–	–
	L3	Spare	–	–	–	–	–

Notes

Figure 2

Conductor csa	mΩ/m at 20 °C
1.5	12.1
2.5	7.41
4	4.61

21 List

    a) **all** certifying documentation that will need to be completed, relevant to this verification process   (3 marks)

    b) **one** statutory and **two** non-statutory publications that are relevant to the inspection   (3 marks)

    c) **three** items of documentation/information that should be available to the person carrying out the inspection   (3 marks)

    d) **six** items from the Schedule of Inspections relevant to this installation.   (6 marks)

22 List

    a) **five** items of information that must be included on the installation schedule fixed within the distribution board   (10 marks)

    b) **two** warning or danger notices required by BS 7671 that may be present within the installation   (4 marks)

    c) **one** item to be checked relating to the specifications of the circuit-breakers.   (1 mark)

23 A test for continuity of circuit protective conductors is to be carried out on the radial socket-outlet circuit in the office (6L1). The circuit $R_1 + R_2$ value is to be established at the same time.

    a) Explain how this test would be carried out.   (11 marks)

    b) Calculate, using the data given in Figure 1 and Figure 2, the expected test result value in ohms. Show **all** calculations.   (4 marks)

Notes

24 a) Describe briefly how to carry out, by direct measurement, an earth loop impedance test on the workshop lighting circuit (3L3). (8 marks)

b) State an alternative method of obtaining the value if direct measurement is not possible. (3 marks)

c) State how the test results obtained in a) can be verified to ensure the circuit conforms with BS 7671. (4 marks)

25 a) Explain
   i) why it is necessary to provide additional protection, using a 30 mA RCD, for the socket-outlet circuits in the workshop. Some of these sockets are located near the loading bay doors. (5 marks)
   ii) how one of the RCDs in a) would be tested. (9 marks)

b) State how often the RCD test button must be operated in normal service. (1 mark)

26 a) Describe the procedure for carrying out a prospective fault current (PFC) test for this installation. (7 marks)

b) Explain how the PFC for this installation will be determined from the results obtained in a). (3 marks)

c) Explain the significance of the result obtained in b) above. (5 marks)

Notes

Questions and answers

The questions in sample test 2 are repeated below with sample answers and comments and advice where appropriate.

Section A

1 State
   a) one example of installation work that would require an
       Electrical Installation Certificate   (1 mark)
   b) the persons that should retain copies of the certificate in a). (2 marks)

Answer
   a) Installation of a new circuit   (1 mark)
   b) • The person ordering the work   (1 mark)
       • The company carrying out the inspection and test   (1 mark)

Comments
   a) Acceptable alternatives for answer a could include any new circuit
       or circuits, new-build or rewire, or additions and alterations to an
       existing installation.

2 State the purpose of an initial verification of a newly installed
   circuit.   (3 marks)

Answer
   • To confirm that the circuit complies with the designer's
      intentions.   (1 mark)
   • The circuit has been designed, installed and tested in
      accordance with the requirements of BS 7671.   (1 mark)
   • It is not damaged so as to impair safety or otherwise
      defective.   (1 mark)

3 State **three** items that may be inspected, while carrying out an
   initial verification of an installation, when considering fault
   protection provided by automatic disconnection of supply.   (3 marks)

Answer
   • Presence of earthing conductor   (1 mark)
   • Presence of circuit protective conductors   (1 mark)
   • Presence of protective bonding conductors   (1 mark)

Comments

BS 7671 requires that the following are checked when inspecting the provision for fault protection by automatic disconnection of supply:

- presence of earthing conductor
- presence of circuit protective conductors
- presence of protective bonding conductors
- presence of supplementary bonding conductors
- presence of earthing arrangements for combined protective and functional purposes
- presence of adequate arrangements for alternative source(s) where applicable
- FELV
- choice and setting of protective and monitoring devices.

Any three from the above list would be acceptable answers.

Examiner's tip: The use of incorrect terminology when describing the items to be inspected may well result in a loss of marks, so be careful.

4 a) List the **two** documents that must accompany a Periodic Inspection Report. (2 marks)

   b) State **one** piece of information that must be written on a Periodic Inspection Report and agreed with the client prior to testing. (1 mark)

Answer

a) • Schedule of Inspections (1 mark)
    • Schedule of Test Results (1 mark)

b) The extent of the installation to be inspected (1 mark)

Comments

a) The correct titles must be stated.

b) An acceptable alternative for answer b is any limitations, including reasons, placed on the inspection and testing process.

Notes

5   During periodic inspection and testing of an installation the inspector must ensure the safety of persons. State **three** practical actions that the inspector can take in order to maintain a safe environment during this process.   (3 marks)

Answer
- Safely isolate circuits as appropriate and lock off.   (1 mark)
- Inform the people within the building about the work being carried out if it affects their safety.   (1 mark)
- Post warning signs where necessary.   (1 mark)

Comments
Other acceptable answers include erecting barriers, seeking permission to switch off or warning people when the supply is about to be restored.

6   List **three** items of technical information which are to be entered on both an Electrical Installation Certificate and a Periodic Inspection Report.   (3 marks)

Answer
- Type of earthing system   (1 mark)
- Supply voltage   (1 mark)
- Supply frequency   (1 mark)

Comments
There are a number of items of technical information that must be entered on these documents and any three would be acceptable answers. All of the following are acceptable:
- earthing arrangements (type of earthing system)
- number and type of live conductors (a.c./d.c., single- or three-phase)
- nature of supply parameters (supply voltage and frequency, PFC and Z_e)
- supply protective device characteristics
- means of earthing including details of installation earth electrode where relevant
- details of main protective conductors
- cetails of main switch or circuit-breaker.

7 State **three** safety checks to be carried out on an earth fault loop impedance tester and leads prior to conducting a test on a lighting circuit. (3 marks)

Answer
- The probes should have finger guards. (1 mark)
- The probes should be insulated to leave an exposed metal tip not exceeding 4 mm, but preferably not exceeding 2 mm, or have spring-loaded retractable screened probes. (1 mark)
- Leads should be fused and/or contain a suitably rated current limiting resistor. (1 mark)

Comments
Acceptable alternative answers may include the following:
- the leads should be adequately insulated and have sheathing to provide sufficient protection against mechanical protection
- the leads are not too short or too long
- the leads should be inspected for signs of damage
- the outer casing of the instrument should be inspected for signs of damage.

8 A test is to be conducted on an immersion heater circuit to establish the value of $R_1 + R_2$. State
a) the instrument to be used (1 mark)
b) what action must be taken regarding the test leads to obtain an accurate result (1 mark)
c) the meaning of $R_1 + R_2$. (1 mark)

Answer
a) A low-resistance ohmmeter. (1 mark)
b) The resistance of the leads should be noted and deducted from the measured value or nulled. (1 mark)
c) R_1 is the resistance of the line conductor of the circuit and R_2 is the resistance of the protective conductor of the circuit. (1 mark)

9   A ring final circuit continuity test is to be carried out on a newly installed circuit. State
   a)   the instrument to be used   (1 mark)
   b)   **two** additional tests that are automatically carried out when completing this test.   (2 marks)

Answer

a)   A low-resistance ohmmeter.   (1 mark)
b)   • Continuity of protective conductors   (1 mark)
     • Polarity   (1 mark)

Comments

b)   Stating $R_1 + R_2$ would not be an acceptable answer.

10 The insulation resistance of a three-phase installation is to be tested. State
   a)   the conductors between which the test should be carried out   (2 marks)
   b)   the units in which the test is measured.   (1 mark)

Answer

a)   Between live conductors (including the neutral) and between live conductors and earth   (2 marks)
b)   Megohms, $M\Omega$ (1 mark)

Comments

a)   An acceptable answer would be to list all possible test combinations. As the question relates to a three-phase installation this must include all three lines, neutral and earth.

Examiner's tip: Remember that the neutral conductor is a 'live' conductor.

11 State
   a)   **two** physical changes made to an installation that may result in an increase in the resistance of a circuit conductor   (2 marks)
   b)   **one** reason, apart from a fault or deterioration, why overall insulation resistance of an installation may decrease.   (1 mark)

Answer

a)   • Increase in load current   (1 mark)
     • Increase in ambient temperature   (1 mark)
b)   Additional circuit or circuits added   (1 mark)

Comments

a) An alternative answer could include cable surrounded by thermal insulation.
    Examiner's tip: Factors such as high resistance joints and loose connections would not be acceptable answers. These are factors which affect the circuit resistance but not the conductor resistance.

b) An alternative answer could include increase in circuit length or presence of moisture or dirt.

12 BS 7671 identifies protective measures to be used for electrical separation. State
    a) **two** methods of achieving basic protection for electrical separation   (2 marks)
    b) the method of providing fault protection for electrical separation.   (1 mark)

Answer

a) • Insulation of live parts   (1 mark)
    • Barriers or enclosures   (1 mark)
b) Simple separation from other circuits and earth   (1 mark)

13 State
    a) the IP code verified by the use of
        i)   1 mm diameter wire   (1 mark)
        ii) the standard test finger   (1 mark)
    b) the meaning of 'X' in the code IPX4.   (1 mark)

Answer

a) i)   IP4X   (1 mark)
    ii) IPXXB   (1 mark)
b) There is no requirement to specify protection against solid objects entering the enclosure.   (1 mark)

Comments

a) i)   An acceptable alternative answer would be IPXXD.
         As IP2X requires two tests to be made (the other being a 12.5 mm sphere), it cannot be accepted as an answer.

Notes

14 Explain briefly why it is necessary to carry out a polarity test
   on a radial socket-outlet circuit. (3 marks)

Answer
To confirm that:
- wiring has been correctly connected at the consumer unit/
  distribution board (1 mark)
- the fuse/circuit breaker is connected in the line conductor (1 mark)
- the socket-outlets are correctly connected (1 mark)

Comments
Correct connection of fused connection units or other accessories would
be an acceptable alternative answer.

15 State
   a) **two** instruments that may be used when confirming the
      effectiveness of an earth electrode (2 marks)
   b) what action must be taken with regard to the earthing
      conductor during the test. (1 mark)

Answer
a) • Earth electrode resistance tester (1 mark)
   • Earth loop impedance tester (1 mark)
b) It should be disconnected at the main earthing terminal (1 mark)

Comments
b) The purpose of disconnecting the earthing conductor is to ensure
   that the applied test current passes through the earth electrode only
   and not through parallel paths created by bonding arrangements on
   the installation.
   Examiner's tip: Disconnecting the earthing conductor at the electrode
   is an acceptable alternative where an earth electrode resistance
   tester is used, but this instrument must be specified in the answer to
   obtain the mark.

16 A test is to be conducted on an existing installation to establish
   the value of Z_e. State
   a) the instrument to be used (1 mark)
   b) the action to be taken with regard to the
      i) earthing conductor (1 mark)
      ii) supply. (1 mark)

Answer
a) Earth loop impedance tester   (1 mark)
b) i) The earthing conductor must be disconnected to
        remove parallel paths.   (1 mark)
    ii) The supply must be on, but the installation must not
        be energised.   (1 mark)

Comments
During the test the installation is not earthed. It is essential that the installation is not energised while this condition exists. As soon as the test is complete the earthing arrangements must be reinstated.

---

17 The maximum tabulated values of earth loop impedance, given in BS 7671, for **three** circuits are 2.3 Ω, 1.44 Ω and 0.57 Ω. The measured values for these circuits are 1.22 Ω, 0.44 Ω and 0.36 Ω respectively. Determine if the measured values are acceptable. Show **all** calculations.   (3 marks)

Answer
Circuit 1	2.3 x 0.8 = 1.84 Ω	> 1.22 Ω	Pass	(1 mark)
Circuit 2	1.44 x 0.8 = 1.152 Ω	> 0.44 Ω	Pass	(1 mark)
Circuit 3	0.57 x 0.8 = 0.456 Ω	> 0.36 Ω	Pass	(1 mark)

Comments
All three circuits passed using the approximate method given in Appendix 14 of BS 7671, therefore no other assessment is required.

---

18 An RCD to BS EN 61008 is to provide additional protection for 13 A socket-outlets, for use by ordinary persons, intended for general use. State
a) the maximum permitted operating current ($I_{\Delta n}$) of the RCD   (1 mark)
b) the maximum test current when testing the device in a)   (1 mark)
c) the maximum permitted disconnection time for the test in b). (1 mark)

Answer
a) 30 mA   (1 mark)
b) 150 mA   (1 mark)
c) 40 ms   (1 mark)

Comments
b) 5 x $I_{\Delta n}$ is not an acceptable answer for b) as the question requires the actual test current for this device.

Examiner's tip: Read the question carefully. When asked for a test current, state it.

19 List three types of installation where a 300 mA RCD would be installed because a particular risk of fire exists. (3 marks)

Answer
- Woodworking facilities (1 mark)
- Paper mills (1 mark)
- Hay stores (1 mark)

Comments
Suitable alternatives would be any installation where dust and fibres pose a fire risk, such as saw mills or flour mills.

20 The prospective fault current at the origin of a 230 V single-phase installation forming part of a TN-S system is to be measured. State
   a) the conductors between which testing is to be carried out (2 marks)
   b) which result from a) is to be recorded on an Electrical Installation Certificate. (1 mark)

Answer
   a) The prospective short-circuit current is measured between line and neutral. The prospective earth fault current is measured between line and earth. (2 marks)
   b) The highest measured value. (1 mark)

Section B

21 List

   a)   **all** certifying documentation that will need to be completed, relevant to this verification process   (3 marks)

   b)   **one** statutory and **two** non-statutory publications that are relevant to the inspection   (3 marks)

   c)   **three** items of documentation/information that should be available to the person carrying out the inspection   (3 marks)

   d)   **six** items from the Schedule of Inspections relevant to this installation.   (6 marks)

Answer

a)
- Electrical Installation Certificate   (1 mark)
- Schedule of Inspections   (1 mark)
- Schedule of Test Results   (1 mark)

b) **Statutory**
- The Electricity at Work Regulations   (1 mark)

   Non-statutory
- GS38   (1 mark)
- Guidance Note 3   (1 mark)

c)
- Details of general characteristics   (1 mark)
- Relevant chart, diagrams and tables   (1 mark)
- Manufacturers' information relating to items being connected including any items vulnerable to damage during testing   (1 mark)

d)
- Method of providing basic protection   (1 mark)
- Method of providing fault protection   (1 mark)
- Presence of danger notices   (1 mark)
- Prevention of mutual detrimental influence   (1 mark)
- Selection of conductors for current-carrying capacity and voltage drop   (1 mark)
- Erection methods   (1 mark)

Notes

Comments

a) Correct titles of documents must be used to obtain marks.

b) The answer must make it clear which document is statutory and which documents are non-statutory. Other suitable answers could be BS 7671 or the On-Site Guide as non-statutory documents.

c) An alternative answer could have listed three items of information contained in Sections 311, 312 and 313, Assessment of General Characteristics, given in BS 7671. Reference to the design specification would also be an acceptable item.

d) Any six items from the Schedule of Inspections would be acceptable, providing they relate to the scenario. This would exclude items such as SELV, PELV and placing out of reach, for example. Section headings and individual items would be acceptable, but the correct wording is required. The Schedule of Inspections is contained in Appendix 6 of BS 7671.

---

22 List

a) **five** items of information that must be included on the installation schedule fixed within the distribution board   (10 marks)

b) **two** warning or danger notices required by BS 7671 that may be present within the installation   (4 marks)

c) **one** item to be checked relating to the specifications of the circuit-breakers.   (1 mark)

Answer

a)
- Any circuit or equipment vulnerable to testing   (2 marks)
- Type of wiring and number of points served   (2 marks)
- Number and size of conductors   (2 marks)
- Method(s) used to provide basic and fault protection   (2 marks)
- Identification of protective, isolation and switching devices   (2 marks)

b)
- Warning notices for both earthing and bonding connections   (2 marks)
- Periodic inspection notice (indicating when the installation should next be inspected and tested)   (2 marks)

c) The breaking capacity of the protective devices must be at least equal to the prospective fault current.   (1 mark)

Comments

a) For any circuit or equipment, both items are included, as some components form part of the circuit, eg a dimmer switch, while others are items of equipment connected to a circuit.

b) Any suitable warning or danger notice contained in BS 7671 would be an acceptable answer, providing it is appropriate to the scenario.

c) Alternative answers would include circuit-breakers of the correct rating and type to provide protection against overcurrent and to provide fault protection.

---

23 A test for continuity of circuit protective conductors is to be carried out on the radial socket-outlet circuit in the office (6L1). The circuit $R_1 + R_2$ value is to be established at the same time.

a) Explain how this test would be carried out.   (11 marks)

b) Calculate, using the data given in Figure 1 and Figure 2, the expected test result value in ohms. Show **all** calculations.   (4 marks)

Answer

a)
- Safely isolate and lock off   (2 marks)
- Use a low-resistance ohmmeter   (1 mark)
- Check the instrument is working   (1 mark)
- Null leads, or note resistance of leads   (1 mark)
- Link line and cpc at the distribution board   (1 mark)
- Test between line and cpc at each socket   (1 mark)
- Record the highest reading as the $R_1 + R_2$ value for the circuit, subtracting resistance of leads if necessary   (1 mark)
- Remove test link   (2 marks)
- Reinstate circuit   (1 mark)

b) Expected $R_1 + R_2$ value =

$$\frac{\text{circuit length x m}\Omega\text{/m value}}{1000} = \frac{20 \times 2 \times 4.61}{1000} = \frac{184.4}{1000} = 0.1844\ \Omega$$

(1 mark)   (2 marks)   (1 mark)

Notes

Comments

a) Identifying the circuit would be the first step in this procedure. However, this has been identified in the question and therefore omitted from the answer. Certain aspects of the answer (safe isolation and locking off, and removing the test link) have significant safety implications, and therefore carry extra marks.
Examiner's tip: Using bullet points rather than writing out an essay saves time and helps produce a logical procedure.

Examiner's tip: Although a drawing/diagram is not asked for here, it could be used to help you to answer the question, if you find this is a method that works well for you. Below is how the question could be answered by incorporating a diagram. Note though that the diagram will only secure you two marks, so if it will take more than two minutes to draw, it is not worth the time.

a) • Safely isolate and lock off   (2 marks)
    • Use a low-resistance ohmmeter   (1 mark)
    • Check the instrument is working   (1 mark)
    • Null leads   (1 mark)
    • Connect as diagram   (2 marks)

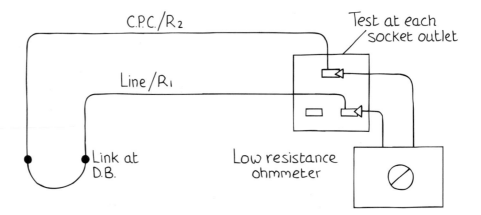

    • Record the highest reading as the $R_1 + R_2$ value for the circuit   (1 mark)
    • Remove test link   (2 marks)
    • Reinstate circuit   (1 mark)

b) Marks are awarded for showing the formula, calculation and final answer. As both line and cpc conductors are the same size in this circuit, the conductor resistance may be doubled (x 2). Where different csa line and cpc conductors are used, the calculation must be done for each conductor and the results added together to obtain $R_1 + R_2$.
Examiner's tip: Make sure you read the question. All calculations must be shown to gain full marks.

---

24 a) Describe briefly how to carry out, by direct measurement, an earth loop impedance test on the workshop lighting circuit (3L3). (8 marks)
b) State an alternative method of obtaining the value if direct measurement is not possible. (3 marks)
c) State how the test results obtained in a) can be verified to ensure the circuit conforms with BS 7671. (4 marks)

Answer
a) • Secure safe area around the last luminaire on the circuit (2 marks)
   • Test instrument to be used is an earth loop impedance tester (1 mark)
   • Leads to GS38 (1 mark)
   • At the furthest point on the circuit test between switched line and cpc (1 mark)
   • With the circuit energised, test and record result (2 marks)
   • Reinstate the luminaire (1 mark)

b) By calculation from $Z_s = Z_e + (R_1 + R_2)$ (3 marks)

c) The test result can be compared with the table values in BS 7671 using a 0.8 factor. (2 marks)
   The measured value must not exceed the BS 7671 table value multiplied by 0.8. (2 marks)

Comments
a) Examiner's tip: Using bullet points rather than an essay saves time and helps produce a logical procedure. Drawings are often helpful in the explanation and can be used even when they are not asked for in the question.

Notes

c) As this question is only worth four marks, it is not necessary to go into great detail as to the method of carrying out the more detailed assessment of the test result. Remember, you have one minute for each mark. If the question required an answer covering the detailed assessment procedure this would be made clear and the answer would have been worth more marks.

Examiner's tip: Ensure you read the question fully before answering, as there is a danger of giving too much detail in the first part of the question when that information is required later.

25 a) Explain
   i) why it is necessary to provide additional protection, using a 30 mA RCD, for the socket-outlet circuits in the workshop. Some of these sockets are located near the loading bay doors. (5 marks)
   ii) how one of the RCDs in a) would be tested. (9 marks)
   b) State how often the RCD test button must be operated in normal service. (1 mark)

Answer

a) i) Additional protection is required for socket-outlets having a rating not exceeding 20 A that may be used by ordinary persons for general use. (3 marks)
      Socket-outlets may supply mobile equipment used outdoors. (2 marks)

   ii) • Using RCD tester with suitable plug-in lead (1 mark)
       • Test at convenient socket-outlet (1 mark)
       • 5 x $I_{\Delta n}$ (150 mA) at both half-cycles (1 mark)
       • Disconnection in 40 ms (1 mark)
       • 1 x $I_{\Delta n}$ (30 mA) at both half-cycles (1 mark)
       • Disconnection in 300 ms (1 mark)
       • ½ x $I_{\Delta n}$ (15 mA) at both half-cycles (1 mark)
       • No disconnection (1 mark)
       • Operate test button (1 mark)

b) Quarterly (1 mark)

Comments

a) ii) The question did not ask for a sequence so, providing the three tests are given, marks will be awarded.
       Examiner's tip: Using bullet points rather than an essay saves time and helps produce a logical procedure.

26	a)	Describe the procedure for carrying out a prospective fault current (PFC) test for this installation.	(7 marks)
	b)	Explain how the PFC for this installation will be determined from the results obtained in a).	(3 marks)
	c)	Explain the significance of the result obtained in b) above.	(5 marks)

Answer

a)
- Secure safe area around the distribution board (2 marks)
- Test instrument to be used is a PFC tester (1 mark)
- Leads to GS38 (1 mark)
- With the supply on and installation isolated (1 mark)
- At the distribution board test between each line conductor and neutral (1 mark)
- Test between each line conductor and earth (1 mark)

b) Multiply the highest line to neutral value obtained in a) by 2 to obtain the three-phase prospective short-circuit current, which is the PFC. (3 marks)

c) The value of the maximum breaking capacity of the circuit breakers fitted within the distribution board should not be less than the value recorded during the test in b). (5 marks)

Comments

a) If a three-phase prospective fault current test instrument is used, then the procedure must be appropriate for that particular instrument.

Notes

More information

More
information

Notes

Further reading

BS 7671: 2008 Requirements for Electrical Installations, IEE Wiring Regulations Seventeenth Edition, published by the IEE, London, 2008

On-Site Guide: BS 7671: 2008, published by the IEE, London, 2008

The Electrician's Guide to Good Electrical Practice, published by Amicus, 2005

Electrician's Guide to the Building Regulations, published by the IEE, London, 2005

IEE Guidance Notes, a series of guidance notes, each of which enlarges upon and amplifies the particular requirements of a part of the *IEE Wiring Regulations, Seventeenth Edition*, published by the IEE, London:
– Guidance Note 1: *Selection and Erection of Equipment*, 5th Edition 2008
– Guidance Note 2: *Isolation and Switching*, 5th Edition 2008
– Guidance Note 3: *Inspection and Testing*, 5th Edition 2008
– Guidance Note 4: *Protection Against Fire*, 5th Edition 2008
– Guidance Note 5: *Protection Against Electric Shock*, 5th Edition 2008
– Guidance Note 6: *Protection Against Overcurrent*, 5th Edition 2008
– Guidance Note 7: *Special Locations*, 3rd Edition 2008
– Guidance Note 8: *Earthing and Bonding*, 2007

Brian Scaddan, *Electrical Installation Work*, published by Newnes (an imprint of Butterworth-Heinemann), 2002

John Whitfield, *Electrical Craft Principles*, published by the IEE, London, 1995

Online resources

City & Guilds www.cityandguilds.com
The City & Guilds website can give you more information about studying for further professional and vocational qualifications to advance your personal or career development, as well as locations of centres that provide the courses.

Institution of Engineering and Technology (IET) www.theiet.org
The Institution of Engineering and Technology was formed by the amalgamation of the Institution of Electrical Engineers (IEE) and the Institution of Incorporated Engineers (IIE). It is the largest professional engineering society in Europe and the second largest of its type in the world. The Institution produces the *IEE Wiring Regulations* and a range of supporting material and courses.

SmartScreen www.smartscreen.co.uk
City & Guilds' dedicated online support portal SmartScreen provides learner and tutor support for over 100 City & Guilds qualifications. It helps engage learners in the excitement of learning and enables tutors to free up more time to do what they love the most – teach!

BRE Certification Ltd www.partp.co.uk

British Standards Institution www.bsi-global.com

CORGI Services Ltd www.corgi-gas-safety.com

ELECSA Ltd www.elecsa.org.uk

Electrical Contractors' Association (ECA) www.eca.co.uk

Joint Industry Board for the Electrical Contracting Industry (JIB)
www.jib.org.uk

NAPIT Certification Services Ltd www.napit.org.uk

National Inspection Council for Electrical Installation Contracting (NICEIC) www.niceic.org.uk

Oil Firing Technical Association for the Petroleum Industry (OFTEC)
www.oftec.co.uk

Notes

Further courses

City & Guilds Level 3 Certificate in the Requirements for Electrical Installations BS 7671: 2008 (2382-10)

This qualification is aimed at practising electricians with relevant experience and is intended to ensure that they are conversant with the format, content and application of BS 7671: Requirements for Electrical Installations, 17th Edition.

City & Guilds Level 3 Certificate in the Code of Practice for In-Service Inspection and Testing of Electrical Equipment (2377)

This course, commonly known as PAT/Portable Appliance Testing, is for staff undertaking and recording inspection and testing of electrical equipment. The course includes a practical exercise. Topics covered include equipment construction, inspection and recording, combined inspection and testing, and equipment.

City & Guilds Level 2 Certificate in Fundamental Inspection, Testing and Initial Verification (2392-10)

This qualification provides candidates with an introduction to the initial verification of electrical installations. It is aimed at practising electricians who have not carried out inspection and testing since qualifying, those who require update training and those with limited experience of inspection and testing. Together with suitable on-site experience, it also prepares candidates to go on to the Level 3 Certificate in Inspection, Testing and Certification of Electrical Installations (2391-10).

City & Guilds Building Regulations for Electrical Safety

This new suite of qualifications is for Competent Persons in Domestic Electrical Installations (Part P of the Building Regulations). The qualifications consist of components for specialised domestic building regulations and domestic wiring regulations routes as well as a component for Qualified Supervisors.

JIB Electrotechnical Certification Scheme (ECS) Health and Safety Assessment

This Health and Safety Assessment is a requirement for electricians wishing to work on larger construction projects and sites in the UK and the exam is an online type very similar in format to the GOLA tests. It is now a mandatory requirement for holding an ECS card, and is a requirement for all members of the ECS. Please refer to www.jib.org.uk/ecs2.htm for details.